Borderline Personality Disorder

Understanding Borderline Personality Disorder, and how it can be managed, treated, and improved

Table of Contents

Introduction

Thank you for taking the time to pick up this book on Borderline Personality Disorder!

This book covers the topic of Borderline Personality Disorder and will educate you on the many signs and symptoms, challenges, and struggles that come with BPD. You will discover what things can cause Borderline Personality Disorder to develop in the first place, as well as how it is diagnosed.

Further, this book will educate you on the different treatment options that are commonly used to combat and overcome BPD. You'll also be given a range of strategies for helping a loved one who is suffering with BPD.

Keep in mind, that this book should not be taken as medical advice. You should always seek the help of a medical professional. The aim of this book is simply to educate you on Borderline Personality Disorder, help you to better understand how BPD effects a person, and let you know what the best treatment options are considered to be.

Once again, thanks for choosing this book, I hope you find it to be helpful!

Chapter 1: What Is Borderline Personality Disorder?

Princess Diana was one of the most popular and loved English aristocrats. She had a beautiful face, a great posture, and a captivating presence.

Lady Diana Spencer was born into a wealthy aristocratic family. She had a sheltered life. She was shy, but she was interested in dancing and performing. She went to a boarding school in Switzerland. She also taught children at Young England Kindergarten.

The People's Princess captivated the hearts of the masses, not only in the United Kingdom, but all over the world. The paparazzi chased her everywhere she went. Princess Di was sweet and kind, and she always knows what to say and when to say it. She had a colorful, beautiful, wealthy, and remarkable life.

After the princess died in a car crash, renowned writer Sally Bedell Smith interviewed one hundred and fifty people who personally knew her, including known British journalists. Smith then wrote a book that revealed the princess' dark side.

Diana was a branding and marketing genius. She managed to appear as the perfect and sympathetic princess. But she has a secret life. Diana was lonely, bulimic, and suicidal. She had a sexless marriage. She also frequently threw childlike tantrums. Sally Bedell Smith claimed that the People's Princess has a mental health disorder called Borderline Personality Disorder, or BPD for short.

For the first time in history, people got interested in BPD. But Princess Diana's condition was not uncommon at all. In fact, over 4 million people have been diagnosed with BPD in the United States alone.

Borderline Personality Disorder is defined by an instability of self-image and interpersonal relationships. It is characterized by unstable functioning, moods, and behavior, which results in impulsivity, relationship issues, depression, anger, and anxiety. It's often triggered by a traumatic childhood experience.

When you have BPD, it's like you live on the edge all the time. You feel intense emotions most of the day – happiness, sadness, euphoria, depression. You may engage in self-harming behavior, including impulsive spending, gambling, unsafe sex, and drug use. It can even lead to suicide in some cases.

Borderline Personality Disorder is something that people do not often talk about, so it's frequently misunderstood. It's also hard to diagnose as it overlaps with other mental health issues, such as depression and eating disorders.

What's the Difference between BPD and Depression?

While they may appear to be closely similar, there are factors that differentiate BPD from depression. BPD stems from poor emotion regulation. This means that people with BPD don't know how to control their emotions. This is the reason why they're often seen as unstable. This mental illness creates a cocktail of depression, resentment, anger, and anxiety. Imagine how tiring it is to feel waves of negative emotions on a daily basis. When you have BPD, it can feel like you're riding an emotional roller coaster. But, if you're depressed, you typically feel only one emotion all the time – sadness.

If you have Borderline Personality Disorder, you could feel anger one minute and then, you'll feel relieved and then, depressed. And then you may become anxious, before feeling some other way a moment later. It's like you're riding a scary emotional roller coaster.

Another similar mental condition is Bipolar Disorder. BPD and Bipolar Disorder are similar in terms of the fluctuating emotions. The difference between the two is that people who have bipolar disorder experience breaks between emotions. For example, a depending on the type of Bipolar Disorder, a bipolar person may experience euphoria for six months straight and then, his emotions could stabilize for two months. Then, they could experience depression for the next six months. A person with BPD, on the other hand, would many experience different emotions in the one day. There's no break.

BPD: The Most Stigmatized Mental Health Problem

The term "borderline" was used to describe this condition because early psychotherapists believed that what people with BPD were experiencing lied on the border between psychosis and neurosis. This is because they are sometimes out of touch of reality. They worry about irrational things. They are constantly paranoid and thinking that everybody is out to get them. They are often seen as unstable. This is the reason why people with BPD are stigmatized as "crazy." People with BPD are often stereotyped as overly dramatic, manipulative, and attention-seekers.

But, the truth is, people with BPD are not bad. They are just in constant pain and confusion. They feel intense emotions all the time. And so, many do anything they can to numb this pain – cut their skin, attempt suicide, max out their credit card, binge eat, or drink themselves silly.

People with BPD do not need judgment. They are crying for help.

Symptoms of Borderline Personality Disorder

People with BPD can be in pain a lot of the time because of their irrational thoughts. Many sufferers feel a constant fear of being abandoned, and this makes them think irrationally. They may think, or act illogically, such as in the following examples:

• "It's 7:10 pm. He said he was going to be here at 7:00 pm. He doesn't like me. I don't think anyone will like me. I am a loser. I am going to break up with him before he abandons me."

•"I hate you so much, but please don't leave me. I'll kill myself if you leave me."

• "Why can't I find my keys? I am so stupid. I am going to spend the next 30 minutes crying and screaming because life is not fair."

It's not easy living with BPD. You can feel like you don't have a purpose. Many feel that their existence doesn't matter, and so they engage in romantic and sexual relationships to fill that void. They may constantly struggle with anxiety, depression, and intense anger. Tantrums and mood swings can create conflict between the sufferer, their co-workers, family members, boss, and even their neighbors.

And most of all, people with BPD will struggle with low self-esteem day in and day out. To summarize what a BPD sufferer may experience on a daily basis, below are the most common BPD symptoms:

Intense Fear of Abandonment

People with BPD have intense fear of abandonment because they have low self-esteem. They may have constant feelings of unworthiness, and as a result they worry that people in their life will leave them.

Unstable Self-Image

People with BPD often have identity problems. You see, your self-identity is how you see yourself. When you have a stable self-image, you see yourself consistently in the same way, despite of the fact that you may behave in contradictory ways sometimes.

People who don't have a strong sense of self-identity can transform into a different person at every stage of their life. Who they are in the past is different from who they are now, and who they will be in the future. Some people feel like they transform into a different person on a daily basis.

Remember that your identity is your perception of what you are – your dreams, preferences, values, beliefs, and hobbies. But, sometimes, external factors can challenge your identity, like moving to a new country, switching jobs, graduating from college, or even getting married.

It's natural to grow and evolve over time. However, people with BPD will change the way they view themselves on a regular basis. This can cause a lot of issues in their lives.

If you don't have a strong sense of identity, you'll have a hard time living an authentic life. This can lead to codependent relationships, and destructive people-pleasing behavior.

Emotional Instability

People with BPD change moods faster than they change clothes. They're cheerful one minute, and then, suddenly they get mad over something trivial.

Feeling of Emptiness

People with BPD may feel like there's something missing in their life, like there's a void inside them. They can feel like they don't understand their purpose and they do not know where they are headed. This void is often filled with unhealthy codependent and people-pleasing behaviors.

Impulsive and Self-Destructive Behaviors

People with Borderline Personality Disorder get overwhelmed easily and so, they often engage in impulsive and self-destructive behaviors to cope with this stress. They can engage in self-destructive and impulsive behaviors, such as binge eating, shopping sprees, reckless driving, unprotected sex, fighting, and shoplifting.

Self-harm and Suicidal Behavior

Due to the unstable emotions that a person with BPD experiences, some resort to self-harm. Some with particularly advanced and extreme conditions even resort to suicide.

Paranoia

People with BPD often have irrational thoughts called cognitive distortions. They think thoughts such as "Someone's talking behind my back", "Something bad is going to happen today", "She's only after my money", or "He's going to leave me".

These irrational thoughts can lead to unstable relationships and can reduce your productivity. They can also keep you from building genuine friendships and taking career risks.

Unstable Relationships

People with BPD go through cycles of idealization and devaluation in relationships because of their intense fear of rejection. Let's say that you have BPD, and you really like a colleague. Then, you see them with another person. This could stir up your fear of rejection, even if you aren't in a romantic relationship with your colleague. You might feel inadequate, jealous, and rejected. And so, you start to devalue your colleague. You stop taking their calls, and start to pick fights with them.

Dissociation

People with BPD use dissociation as a coping mechanism. They distance themselves from reality when they're facing challenging and extremely stressful situations. They detach from their emotions and have an unclear sense of identity.

Chapter 2: The Common Causes of BPD

BPD can be caused by a combination of different factors, such as:

1. Genetics

This may seem unfair. But, if one or both of your parents have BPD, you are also most likely to get it. Also, if your twin has it, there's a huge chance that you also have it.

2. Chemical Imbalance

Neurotransmitters like serotonin are messengers that pass signals between brain cells. Having low levels of serotonins can lead to negative thoughts, low self-esteem, mood swings, irritability, difficulty controlling urges, depression, and other BPD symptoms.

3. Brain Development Problems

Brain scans show that people with BDP have a smaller amygdala, hippocampus, and orbitofrontal cortex. The orbitofrontal cortex is used for decision-making and planning. The hippocampus helps regulate your behavior and instills self-control. The amygdala, on the other hand, regulates negative emotions, such as aggression, anxiety, and fear. So, it's no wonder that people with BPD have intense emotions and have a problem controlling their impulses, behaviors, and urges.

4. Environmental Factors

Studies show that distressing and traumatic childhood experiences involving care-givers can lead to emotional instability. These experiences can include:

- ☐ Abandonment and neglect of caregivers

- ☐ Early separation from parents

- ☐ Emotional neglect

- ☐ Physical and emotional abuse

- ☐ Sexual abuse

How Is BPD Diagnosed?

BPD is one of the most misdiagnosed mental health issues because its symptoms are quite similar to other mental health conditions, such as Depression, Anxiety, and Bipolar Disorder.

BPD is diagnosed by a licensed mental health professional such as a psychotherapist or a psychologist. The therapist will usually observe you and ask you some questions to assess your symptoms.

To be diagnosed with BPD, you must have at least five of the following symptoms:

- ☐ Unstable personal relationships

- ☐ Black and white thinking

- ☐ Unclear sense of identity

- ☐ Self-destructive behavior

- ☐ Dissociation

- ☐ Impulsive behavior

- ☐ Uncontrollable emotions

☐   A combination of substance abuse, anger, bad temper, depression, and anxiety

People with BPD usually also have other mental health issues, such as mood disorders (clinical depression and bipolar disorder), anxiety disorders, eating disorders, attention deficit disorder, substance abuse, and dissociative disorders.

Chapter 3: Common Treatments of BPD

Living with BPD can be very challenging. It feels like you're being sucked into a deep black hole of intense emotions, unreasonable fears, false beliefs, and irrational thoughts. But the good news is, BPD can be treated. In this chapter, we will discuss the most common treatment options for BPD.

Dialectical Behavior Therapy

Dialectical Behavior Therapy is a type of talk therapy. In fact, it's based on Cognitive Behavioral Therapy. This therapy type was developed by renowned American psychologist and author, Marsha Linehan in the 1980s as a result of her own mental illness because, she, too, has Borderline Personality Disorder. When she was in her teens, she would cut herself and use cigarettes to burn her skin. She did all this to numb her emotional pain.

Borderline Personality Disorder was not yet identified at that time, so she was diagnosed with schizophrenia. She was medicated with Thorazine, but it did not work. She was released from a mental hospital in 1963.

In 1967, she prayed at a chapel in Chicago and finally found a way to fight her inner demons. She started to accept who she really was – with all her flaws. This is how she developed the concept of "radical acceptance". And for the first time, she said, "I love myself".

She began feeling well, and that's when she knew that Borderline Personality Disorder was curable and manageable. Years later, she developed Dialectical Behavior Therapy or DBT to help people with BPD and suicidal tendencies.

DBT combines different techniques from different areas of psychology, such as CBT (cognitive behavior therapy), relaxation, mindfulness, and breathing exercises.

What Does Dialectical Mean?

Dialectical means acting on opposing forces. DBT balances two opposing ideas in therapy – change and radical acceptance. The goal of this therapy type is based on Reinhold Niebuhr – it teaches to accept what we cannot change and to change what we can. Practitioners also believe that acceptance is the key to change. For example, you cannot improve your mental and emotional health unless you first accept that you have Borderline Personal Disorder.

Foundations of DBT

As mentioned earlier, DBT uses a combination of different psychotherapy and self-help techniques. It is founded on three concepts and principles, namely:

1. Cognitive Behavior Therapy (CBT)

Cognitive Behavior Therapy is the most popular type of psychotherapy. It is based on the idea that our mental health issues stem from our faulty beliefs.

DBT is grounded on the most basic CBT principles – we can change our habits by changing our thoughts.

Like CBT, Dialectical Behavior Therapy also seeks to change your behavior by correcting your cognitive distortions or false beliefs. For example, people with BPD may feel empty because they think negative thoughts like:

☐ "I have no purpose in life."

☐ "I have no value."

☐ "I have not done anything good in this life."

☐ "I am a failure."

DBT helps people with BPD find meaning in their lives by correcting their faulty thought patterns.

2. Self-Validation

One of the most important components of DBT is self-help or personal support. This means that you have to identify your strengths. You also have to develop positive habits and hobbies like meditation, yoga, or pottery.

3. Support Networks

If you have BPD, you must avoid isolation at all cost. Isolation will only make your condition worse. Having a strong support system can prevent isolation and it can help you learn DBT coping strategies quickly. This is the reason why DBT incorporates group therapy sessions.

How Does It Work?

DBT is a talk therapy, which means that you have to sit in a therapist's office and talk about your emotions and thoughts. But this therapy type has four components —individual therapy, group skills training, phone coaching, and a therapist consultation team.

Usually, the therapist will conduct one on one therapy to assess the patient's suicidal and self-harming behaviors. The therapist will also seek to correct therapy-interfering behaviors such as refusal to cooperate or cancelling therapy sessions at the last minute. The therapist also aims to equip the patient with skills that will help improve the quality of their life. The skills are broken down in to four skill modules – interpersonal effectiveness, mindfulness, distress tolerance, and emotional regulation. This will be discussed in more detail, later.

DBT also has group sessions which usually occur once a week. They usually run for two hours and aim to equip people with BPD the skills needed to manage their symptoms.

Therapy sessions with BPD patients are usually emotionally charged. This is the reason why the "therapist consultation team" is an important component of DBT. This team helps the therapist to process their emotions. Major proponents of DBT believe that therapists need therapy, too.

The last component of DBT is phone coaching. This is usually done after the individual therapy is completed.

Four Skills Modules

DBT equips you with different skills that can help you reduce the symptoms of BPD and improve the quality of your life, namely mindfulness, distress tolerance, emotional regulation, and interpersonal effectiveness skills.

Mindfulness

When you have BPD, you can fall out of touch with reality. You are consumed by your fear and irrational thoughts. You experience intense emotions day in and day out. You constantly judge yourself and can get stuck in a specific emotion.

Mindfulness is the art of living in the present moment. It is the art of calmly accepting your feelings, bodily sensations, and thoughts without judgment. It is based on an ancient Eastern meditation practice and is a popular relaxation technique. It also helps you manage and regulate your emotions.

Mindfulness is beneficial for people with BPD because it decreases depression, stress, and anxiety. It also reduces PSTD symptoms, which is common among people with BPD. It also reduces one's emotional reactiveness and helps cultivate logical responses to stressful and challenging situations.

This ancient practice is not only good for your mental health; it also has a number of physical benefits. It can help improve the quality of your sleep and help reduce chronic pain. It also helps reduce your blood pressure and can alleviate gastrointestinal issues.

Most importantly, mindfulness practice helps you observe your feelings and environment logically. It helps you develop a "Teflon mind" – the ability to let situations and emotions pass without sticking in your mind. Let's say that your spouse forgot to buy the milk you asked for. If you have BPD, you're going to respond emotionally to this situation. You're going to yell. You're going to think negative thoughts like "She forgot to buy milk, she doesn't love me anymore. She's going to leave me".

But, if you practice mindfulness, you'll start to listen to your thoughts and logically assess the situation. You'll think, "Oh maybe she was busy at work today and that's why she forgot the milk, I'll just buy it tomorrow".

Distress Tolerance

People with BPD have a hard time accepting their situation. This is the reason why they have low distress tolerance and have difficulty moving on from tragic life events.

DBT equips you with tools and techniques that you can use to cope with an extremely stressful situation. Here are two mnemonics that will help you remember DBT's distress tolerance strategies:

1. **IMPROVE**

☐   I (Imagery) – Visualization exercises can help you calm down and they can help you relax when faced with a stressful situation.

☐ M (Meaning) – Remember that everything happens for a reason, you have to find meaning in your current situation.

☐ P (Prayer) – There's nothing more relaxing than being connected with the Divine. Praying gives you a sense of hope. It helps you believe that things will get better.

☐ R (Relaxation) – You must find a way to relax even when you are in a difficult situation. You can learn breathing techniques, or you can simply watch a funny YouTube video. These activities can help reduce your stress and help you avoid reacting emotionally to a challenging circumstance.

☐ O (One thing at a time) – It's easy to feel overwhelmed if you're doing a number of different things at the same time. This is the reason why you have to focus on one task at a time.

☐ V (Vacation) – Vacation is truly our favorite "V" word. Going on a vacation helps you take time off from your current situation. It energizes you and it helps you experience something new.

☐ E (Encouragement) – You have to encourage yourself and engage in positive self-talk.

2. ACCEPTS

☐ A (Activities) – When you feel overwhelmed, you have to distract yourself with pleasurable activities. Do something that you enjoy.

☐ C (Contributing) – Helping others will make you feel good about yourself. So, make sure to contribute something to a community.

☐ C (Comparison) – When you feel like it's the end of the world, take time to compare yourself to a less fortunate person. Let's say that you got fired from your job. Instead of thinking about how bad your situation is, think about how lucky you are because you have a roof over your head and you finished college. This means that you have a lot of options.

☐ E (Other Emotions) – When you feel depressed, extremely sad, or angry, you could watch a funny TV show to generate positive emotions. You could spend your lunch break with your funniest co-worker. Do something to consciously change your emotional state.

☐ P (Push Away) – Take a step back when you're in an emotionally charged situation. This will help you cool down.

☐ T (Other Thoughts) –Take a deep breath and think about something else when you're about to throw a tantrum.

☐ Sensations (Other Sensations) - Do something that triggers your senses when you feel intense emotions. This will distract you from your negative feelings. You could take a cold shower or eat a bitter candy.

Emotional Regulation

People with BPD feel intense emotions almost all of the time. They can experience anger, depression, frustration, and anxiety in just a few hours.

DBT equips you with techniques that will help you regulate your emotions. It helps you identify your emotions properly, label them, and control them. It helps you become the master of your thoughts and emotions. And most importantly, it helps you develop the ability to solve your problems logically and let go of your emotional pain.

Interpersonal Effectiveness Skills

Interpersonal effectiveness is your ability to interact with others, assert yourself, and manage conflicts. It is the ability to balance your "needs" and "wants" in a relationship. It also helps you build a strong sense of self-respect and self-mastery.

DBT equips you with important interpersonal effectiveness skills, such as:

- ☐ Active listening
- ☐ How to show interest in other people
- ☐ How to respond to praise and genuine compliments
- ☐ How to respond to criticisms

And most importantly, it increases your assertiveness. It helps you look out for your personal interests.

Here's a few mnemonics that will help you remember the interpersonal effectiveness strategies that can improve your relationships:

1. DEARMAN – These strategies will help you express your preferences and get what you want in your relationships and at work:

☐ D - Describe your current situation as clearly as you can. Use concrete words to express what you want.

☐ E - Express your feelings as calmly as possible. A lot of people with BPD engage in passive aggressive behavior to get what they want. But, guess what? Your loved ones or your boss can read your mind. So, you have to tell them how you feel about the situation.

☐ A - Assert yourself. Do not beat around the bush. Be clear about what you want.

☐ R - Reinforce your position. Reward people who respond well to your requests. State why the other person should give you what you want. Tell them what's in it for them.

☐ M - Mindful – Be mindful of your goal. Don't get sidetracked and lose focus of what you want to achieve.

☐ A - Appear confident. You know what they say – fake it until you make it. Stand tall and maintain eye contact. Dress appropriately for every occasion.

☐ N - Negotiate to get what you want. Be willing to compromise to create a "win-win" situation.

2. FAST – These strategies help you cultivate self-respect.

☐ F (Fair) – Be fair to everyone around you. But you should also be fair to yourself. Do not sacrifice your happiness or your welfare just to help other people.

☐ A (Apologies) – Do not apologize unless you need to. You have the right to disagree and to express your real opinion.

☐ S (Stick) to your values – Do not compromise your values and principles, just to please other people.

☐ T (Truthful) – When you have BPD, you may lie to manipulate others or get them to do what you want. But, lying is a sign that you don't respect yourself. To cultivate self-respect, you have to avoid exaggeration and always speak your truth.

3. GIVE –These strategies help you build meaningful relationships.

☐ G (Gentle) – Be gentle when you're communicating with the people around you. Do not attack. Do not yell. Learn how to communicate in a loving and respectful way.

☐ I (Interested) – Show interest in other people's lives. Listen to what they have to say.

☐ V (Validate) – Acknowledge your loved one's feelings and respect their opinions, even they're different from yours.

☐ E (Easy) – Cultivate a light-hearted attitude. Be easy to be with.

The Four Stages of DBT Treatment

DBT treatment is divided into 4 stages of treatment according to the severity of the client's symptoms and behaviors.

Stage 1– This is the stage when the patient is miserable and feels like they're losing control over their life. They may try to kill themselves, use drugs, or engage in other self-destructing behaviors. They feel like they're living in hell.

Stage 2 – During this stage, the patient is able to control their suicidal behavior. But they still feel miserable. They're still in pain. The therapist usually helps the patient identify and correct their faulty points during this stage.

Stage 3 – In this stage, the therapist helps the patient learn how to live. They will help the patient define life goals and increase self-respect, self-esteem, self-confidence, peace, and happiness.

Stage 4 – This stage involves some kind of spiritual experience like what happened to Dr. Marsha Linehan. At this time, the patient may seek to build a connection with the Divine Energy. The goal of this stage is to help the patient achieve happiness, and sense of completeness through spiritual fulfillment.

Therapists usually use formatted diary cards to track the patient's behavior and progress. Dialectical Behavior Therapy is one of the most effective treatments for people with BPD. It increases your resilience and helps you manage your emotions. It also helps you create meaningful, happy, and mutually beneficial relationships.

Mentalization-Based Therapy

Mentalization-Based Therapy is one of the newer types of psychotherapy, and it integrates the principles of cognitive behavioral therapy, the psychodynamic approach, ecological psychological approach, and systemic approach. It was developed by Anthony Bateman and Peter Fonagy especially for people with Borderline Personality Disorder.

But what is mentalization? Well, it's the capacity to "think about thinking". It's the capacity to look inside yourself and process your feelings. When you mentalize, you think about your emotions, thoughts, and where all these thoughts and emotions come from.

For example, let's say that you're angry because your assistant failed to do something that you told her to do. Now, to prevent yourself from lashing out at your poor assistant, you must mentalize. You must ask yourself why you're angry. Are you angry because that task is important? Or, are you angry because you felt that it was disrespectful? Do you feel like your assistant is undermining your authority? Did they open your old emotional wounds, or maybe they uncovered your insecurities?

You can also mentalize about others. You can think about why a friend is asking too many questions, or why your spouse always comes home late. You can try to understand them by thinking about what's going on in their mind.

Let's say that you are a barista in a coffee shop and your customer is rude. If you don't mentalize, you'll just end up shouting back at your customer. Mentalizing help you empathize. For example, when you try to understand your customer's bad behavior you may think "Oh, maybe he's just having a bad day at work" or "Maybe he's going through something, and that's why he's rude and irritable".

Poor mentalizing can lead to poor relationships. Mentalizing is the ability to understand misunderstanding. It's the ability to interpret human behavior in terms of beliefs, intention, desires, and circumstance. It's the process of understanding your and other people's behavior. Mentalization is at the heart of mindfulness, emotional intelligence, and empathy.

Mentalization helps you understand how you contribute to your problems and conflicts with other people. It helps you calm down when you are upset, and it helps you change your behavior. It helps increase your empathy and compassion. It also helps you cope with conflict.

The therapist will encourage you to think about your present situation, so you could change the thoughts and behaviors that are causing your problems.

MBT is usually done twice a week – the first one is individual treatment and the second one is a group session. It's a long-term treatment, and usually lasts 12 to 18 months.

Medications

Therapy is the best treatment for people with Borderline Personality Disorder. As of writing, the FDA has not approved any medications as treatment for BPD. But, since borderline people also experience depression and anxiety, psychotherapists may prescribe anti-anxiety drugs and antidepressants. Some doctors may also use anti-psychotic drugs and mood stabilizers to help manage paranoid thinking and reduce anxiety.

Here's a list of medications that are commonly prescribed to people with BPD:

1. Flouxetine (Prozac)

Flouxetine is a type of serotonin reuptake inhibitor (or SSRI). It is one of the most popular antidepressants in the United States. It is used to treat Anxiety, Depression, and Obsessive-Compulsive Disorder. But you have to be careful. Studies show that Fluoxetine can increase suicidal thoughts, and it also increases anxiety and nervousness. It can also decrease your libido.

2. Phenelzine (Nardil)

Phenelzine is an antidepressant. It improves your mood and it improves your overall well-being. It balances the neurotransmitters in your brain. However, like all the other antidepressants, this drug also has a string of nasty side effects.

3. Venlafaxine (Effexor)

Like many other SSRIs, this drug helps improve your mood and can restore your interest in daily activities, while also helping to reduce your fear and anxiety. But this drug can also cause fatigue and confusion. In some, it can create sensations that are similar to an electric shock.

4. Haloperidol (Haldol)

This is an anti-psychotic drug that decreases one's excitement. It is used to treat Schizophrenia, but some doctors use this drug to reduce the symptoms of BPD. It reduces feelings of excitement. It is used to reduce anger and tantrums. But, like the other drugs in this list, it has a number of side effects, such as dry mouth, nervousness, and diarrhea.

5. Clozapine (Clorazil)

This is an anti-psychotic drug that's usually used to treat someone with Schizophrenia. It reduces the risk of suicide in people with BPD. But you should not take this if you have a heart disease or a brain tumor as this can cause seizures. Also, you must avoid this drug if you have a liver or kidney disease. And it's important that you don't smoke while you are taking this drug.

6. Alprazolam (Xanax)

Xanax is one of the most popular anti-anxiety drugs. It calms your nervous system and helps you feel relaxed even if you are in a challenging situation.

7. Diazepam (Valium)

Valium is used to treat alcohol withdrawal, anxiety, and seizures. It is used to relieve muscle spasms and help calm the nerves. It's useful for people with anxiety, but it can be helpful for borderline people.

8. Lamotrigine (Lamictal)

This prevents seizures and it helps prevent mood swings. This drug is usually used to treat Bipolar Disorder. But this drug is also helpful for people with BPD because they also experience rapid mood swings.

Remember that the FDA has not approved any drug as treatment for BPD. This is the reason why drugs should be the last option. And if you do take medications, it's important to supplement it with therapy.

Chapter 4: Self Help Tips for BPD

Therapy and medications can only do so much. To improve your condition, you have to learn to manage your own symptoms. Below are some self-help tips that you can use to regulate your emotions, prevent self-destructing behaviors, and live a more peaceful and happy life.

Challenge Your "Black And White" Thoughts

Here's the truth – the world is not just black and white; there are a lot of gray areas. This is the reason why you should challenge your all or nothing mindset.

Let's say that you are fired from your job. That's devastating, right? Now, when something like this happens, take a moment to listen to your thoughts. If you catch yourself telling yourself things like "it's the end of the world" or "I will not find another job", take a deep breath. Now ask yourself, are these thoughts even true? Is it really the end of the world just because you lost your job?

It's just a job. You can always get another one. Plus, losing your job can actually be a blessing because now you might have the time to pursue the things that you are truly passionate about. It's all about the way you choose to think about a situation.

Practice Mindfulness Meditation

As discussed earlier in this book, mindfulness is one of the most effective techniques that you can use to manage your BPD symptoms. It reduces symptoms of depression, and it's a great stress management strategy. It also helps you control your impulsive behavior.

To do this:

☐ Sit in a quiet room. You can sit on a cushion or a chair.

☐ Close your eyes and take deep breaths. Inhale from your nose and exhale from your mouth. Make a hissing sound as you breathe out.

☐ Clear your mind. Don't think of anything else. Just focus on your breath. Observe how your chest goes up and down as you breathe. Release all your worries and anxieties.

☐ Now as you breathe in say "I am in control of my emotions" and as you breathe out, say "I accept myself for who I am". Repeat this process at least fifteen times.

☐ Relax every part of your body.

Practice meditation at least once a day for at least five minutes. Try to empty your mind of all thoughts, and just focus on your breathing, and the present moment.

Live in the Present Moment

It's not enough that you practice mindfulness meditation at least once a day. You should also practice mindfulness every minute of your day. This means that you have to try your best to live in the present moment. Forgive those who have hurt you in the past and appreciate the simple joys of life.

Living in the present moment helps you let go of all your worries and anxieties, it also helps you manage your addictions and impulses.

Say Affirmations

BPD is usually associated with low self-esteem. To increase your self-confidence and self-worth, you have to engage in positive self-talk. The best way to do this is to say affirmations.

Face the mirror every morning when you wake up and say these affirmations:

- ☐ I am enough.
- ☐ I am a catch.
- ☐ I am bigger than my emotions.
- ☐ I can control my impulses.
- ☐ I am in control of myself and my life.
- ☐ I am a good person.
- ☐ I can control my anger.
- ☐ I will seek to understand the people around me.
- ☐ I radically accept myself for who I am.
- ☐ I am capable.
- ☐ I can solve my problems.
- ☐ I choose to forgive.
- ☐ I choose to let go of all my anger.
- ☐ I let go of all my pain.
- ☐ I deserve happiness and peace.

The "1 to 5" Approach

When you're about to lash out at someone, take a deep breath and count slowly from one to five. This technique helps you manage and process your strong emotions. It keeps you from screaming at someone over something trivial.

Don't Sweat the Small Stuff

The things that annoy or worry you now won't matter five years from now.

Accept Yourself Completely

Do you spend your days wishing that you were taller, slimmer, or more confident? You're not the only one. But if you want to live a happy and peaceful life, you have to be comfortable in your own skin. You may not see it, but you're perfect just the way you are.

Exercise Regularly

As mentioned earlier in this book, chemical imbalance is one of the common causes of BPD. Aerobic exercises such as dancing, biking, and running increases the serotonin levels in your brain, making you calmer, happier, and more fulfilled.

Do Something That Gives You a Strong Sense of Purpose

When you have BPD, you'll feel empty most of the time. To prevent this, you have to do something that that gives you a sense of purpose. You can volunteer or do something that helps people.

Find Value in What You Do

It can be easy to think of your job as menial. Try to combat this by focusing on what positive impact you do have in your work. Whose day do you make better by working? What service do you provide? What contribution does your work make to the greater society? Focus on these things and strive to think positively about your work.

Set Goals

Your emotions can constantly distract you if you're suffering from BPD. This can get you stuck and keep you from moving forward. This is the reason why you have to set concrete goals. This will give you a sense of purpose and hope. But, make sure that your goals are achievable, realistic, time-bound, and specific.

Share Your Talent with the World

Whenever you feel like you're worthless, think about the things that you are good at, and share your talent with the people around you.

Distract Yourself

When you're thinking negatively, do something to distract yourself. Watch a movie, phone a friend, or go for a run.

Visualize

Visualization can distract you from your strong emotions and difficult situations. It helps release your stress.

Whenever you feel like everything is too much to handle, go to the bathroom or anywhere private. Close your eyes and imagine that you're lying on the beach, feeling totally relaxed and calm.

Hold this vision for as long as you can. Take deep breaths while you're holding this image.

This exercise helps you manage your stress and other strong emotions.

Pray

Prayer is one of the most powerful tools that you can use to manage your BPD. Not everyone is religious, but choosing to ask for help from a higher power makes a lot of people feel more confident in their ability to manage their BPD symptoms.

Avoid Multitasking

We live in a world where multitasking is unfortunately seen as a positive thing by many, but this isn't the truth. You'll get easily overwhelmed if you try to do a lot of things at the same time. Simply focus on one task at a time.

Do One Thing That Makes You Happy Every Single Day

Depression is a common symptom of BPD. To live a happy life, you must incorporate enjoyable and pleasurable activities into your daily schedule.

Here's a list of activities that you can do:

☐   Play with your pet.

☐   Laugh with your friends.

☐   Walk around the park.

☐   Play a team sport.

☐   Arrange flowers or build a garden.

☐   Listen to music.

Listen to Others

When you have BPD, you can get so caught up with your own drama that you often forget to listen to other people. If you want to build meaningful relationships, you have to seek to understand the people around you, and the best way to do that is to just listen.

Challenge Your Paranoid Thoughts

Paranoia can keep you from building meaningful relationships. This is the reason why you should challenge your paranoid thoughts. When you think something like "Everybody is trying to hurt me". You have to challenge that thought. Is there proof that everybody is plotting against you? Why would people want to destroy you? Do you have some kind of evidence?

Challenging your paranoid thoughts helps you think more logically.

Learn to Laugh At Yourself

We all make mistakes. We all screw up at some point of your life. Learn to laugh at yourself. Adopt a light-hearted attitude. Smile more and spread joy to everyone around you.

Eat Foods That Are Rich in Omega 3 Fatty Acids

Omega 3 Fatty Acids deficiency is linked with Bipolar Disorder, ADHD, and Depression. These fatty acids are also beneficial for those diagnosed with BPD.

Consume at least 1000 mg of Omega 3 each day to help manage the symptoms of your BPD. You can take supplements, or you can simply eat foods that are rich in Omega 3, such as walnuts, salmon, flax seed, and hemp seed.

Take A Vacation

Taking a vacation is a great way to reset, and to reduce your stress. So, set aside some of your money and go on a trip at least twice a year.

Connect with the People Around You

Isolation is the worst enemy of people with BPD. It can make you feel alone and can increase the risk of suicide and self-harm. This is why it's important to establish a strong connection with the people around you. Don't hide in your bedroom; see your friends and talk to people you trust. Share your experiences and thoughts. And most of all, do fun things with them.

Drink Yerba Mate Tea

Yerba Mate Tea is called the "happy tea" because it can improve your mood. It's a natural anti-depressant and it's from the beautiful country of Argentina. You can get it from a local health store or online.

Drink A Cup of Valerian Tea

Velerian is known as the "natural Valium". This tea calms you down and helps improve the quality of your sleep.

Try Kava Kava

Kava Kava is one of the best anti-anxiety herbs. It calms you down and helps reduce the intensity of your negative emotions. It gives you a "natural high". This is the reason why you have to be careful in using this herb, as it's regulated in some states.

Set A Regular Sleeping Schedule

Sleeping at least eight hours a night can help prevent emotional outbursts. It can help stabilize your emotions.

Do Something to Distract Yourself from an Intense Emotion

Let's say that you feel frustrated because you lost your car keys. Instead of screaming and crying, take a deep breath and watch a funny, three-minute video on YouTube. This will help to distract yourself from your intense emotions. After watching the video, take a deep breath and start looking for your keys.

Psychoanalyze Yourself

You must take time to psychoanalyze yourself and understand your thoughts and emotions. Why are you angry? Is it because the other person did something wrong, or is it because of your fears? Are your thoughts rational, logical, and evidence-based? Why are you feeling what you're feeling? How you can manage your emotions?

Psychoanalyzing yourself can help you understand your emotions and behaviors, so it's easier for you to regulate them.

Create a Budget

When you have BPD, you're more likely to spend your money irresponsibly, and have trouble saving. This is the reason why you should set a monthly, weekly, and daily budget, and stick to it. This will keep you from going on impulsive shopping sprees.

Chapter 5: How to Help Others with BPD

As mentioned earlier in this book, people with borderline personality disorder have a black and white mindset. This means that they see things as either all good or all bad. Their opinions about the people in their lives can also change rapidly.

People with BPD feel emotions intensely and are overly sensitive. This means that they can be angered easily, and irrationally. They're often reactive, and they take things personally.

Being with someone who has BPD is tough. It can feel like you're walking on eggshells. Below are some strategies that you can use to create a healthier, happier, and more stable relationship with someone with BPD.

Learn As Much As You Can About BPD

You're on the right track because you're reading this book. If your loved one has BPD, it's important to learn as much as you can about BPD. Having a deep understanding about BPD and its symptoms will help you communicate and deal with your loved one in a helpful and more effective way.

Take Care of Yourself First

You can't build a successful and satisfying relationship with someone with BPD unless you take care of yourself first. You need to attend to your physical and emotional needs first before you can take care of another person's emotional needs.

Here's a list of self-care tips that you can use:

1. Focus on your own life.

Make sure that you have a life outside of the relationship. This means that you must have a job that you really like. You should also spend time on activities and interests that you enjoy.

2. Take care of your physical health.

People with BPD are often needy. So, if you're living with one, you might neglect your physical health.

But, if you really want the relationship to work, you have to take care of your own physical health. You should get at least seven hours of sleep a night. You should also practice good hygiene. This is not only good for your health, it also increases your own self-confidence and self-esteem.

3. Build and strengthen your connection with yourself and others.

Creating a genuine connection with another human being is one of our deepest desires. To live a happy life, it's important that you connect with yourself and with the people around you. Set aside at least 30 minutes alone time each day so you can get to know yourself a little bit more. You must also surround yourself with people who lift you up and make you feel good about yourself and the world.

4. Create joy and satisfaction in your life.

Living with someone who has a mental health issue can be taxing and extremely tiring. It can suck out your joy. Before you can take care of someone with BPD, it's important to fill your own life with joy and satisfaction. This means that you have to do the things that make you happy. You must also be on top of your career and finances.

People with BPD already have a chaotic and overly dramatic life. Feeling intense emotions all the time can be tiring. So, to keep yourself from adding drama into your loved one's life, you have to take care of your own needs first.

How to Communicate with Someone who has BPD

Communication is one of the most important components of a relationship. But communicating with someone who has BPD can be extremely challenging because they can be too sensitive. They have difficult reading body language and engaging in non-verbal communication. Also, their intense fear of abandonment can cause them to overreact which can lead to verbal abuse, rage, and violence.

Here's a list of tips that you can use for communicating with someone who has BPD:

1. Listen actively and be sympathetic.

When you're talking to someone who has BPD, it's important that you listen actively. Look into their eyes and nod so they know that you're listening. If they're telling you about how bad their day was, try to sympathize. Be direct. Say you understand and avoid giving advice unless you're asked.

2. Pay attention to your loved one's emotions.

The emotions of a borderline person are not always clear. For example, if they say "I'm fine", don't take their word at face value. Pay attention to their tone and temperament.

3. Stay calm and relaxed, even if your loved one is acting out.

Most borderline people act out their emotions and insecurities. So, when they yell at you or start to call you names, stay calm. Avoid taking things personally and look at the situation objectively. Don't be defensive, just stay cool.

4. Distract your loved one when they're getting emotional.

People with BPD have a habit of blowing things out of proportion. So, if your loved one is angry or sad without any valid reason, try to get them to do soothing activities such as exercising, painting, or playing with a pet.

5. Keep everything simple.

People with BPD constantly react emotionally to most situations. So, when you're speaking your truth, it's hard for them to logically process what you're saying to them. They usually transform simple statements into personal attacks. To prevent fights and drama, you should keep your sentences short, direct, and as void of emotion as possible. This will help your loved one hear and understand you properly.

Do Not Ignore Suicide Threats

When you're pissed off with someone with BPD, it's tempting to just ignore their suicide threats. But, you shouldn't. If you believe that your loved one is at risk, don't leave them alone. Try to respond in a kind and understanding way.

If a borderline person tells you that they are contemplating suicide, don't say something like "don't be stupid" or "you're just doing that to hurt me". Don't freak out. Stay calm. Here's a list of things that you can say to someone who's thinking of committing suicide:

☐ "I'm glad that you told me about your plans." - Your loved one may just need someone who understands them. Someone who will never judge them. This is the reason why you have to reassure them that you understand.

☐ "That's awful. What's happening in your life right now that makes you want to die?" - You have to encourage your loved one to tell you their story. You have to make them feel that it's okay to share, and that you're there to listen without judgment.

☐ "What can I do to help you?" - Assure your loved one that you'll be there for them whenever they need you.

☐ "I care about you." - You would be surprised to know that a lot of people threaten to commit suicide because they feel like no one cares. When you tell a suicidal person that you care, you're giving them hope.

Lastly, encourage professional help. There's only so much that you (and the self-help tools) can do. If you want your loved one's condition to improve, you must encourage them to see mental health professionals.

Remind Your Loved One of Their Strengths

People with BPD have an unstable self-identity. Often, they do not know what their weaknesses are, or even their strengths. No wonder that they have low self-esteem. To help a loved one with BPD, you have to remind them of their strengths. You could say something like:

☐ "I love talking to you because I think that you're witty and funny."

☐ "You are an amazing person and I appreciate you."

☐ "You have a great work ethic and that's something that I appreciate."

☐   "It seems that you have no idea that you're pretty/handsome."

☐   "You deserve that promotion."

☐   "You are fun, and I like being around you."

☐   "I believe in you. I know that you can do it."

☐   "You are good to the kids and I appreciate that."

☐   "Your smile is powerful enough to brighten a room."

☐   "I like that you're kind to strangers."

☐   "You are a great friend."

☐   "You are a good person, you are trying your best every day and I appreciate that."

☐   "I am so proud of how far you've come."

☐   "You make me laugh."

☐   "You may not realize this, but you are a blessing to everyone around you."

☐   "You are stronger than you think."

☐   "I love the way you think. You have great ideas."

☐   "You are a great cook."

☐   "I appreciate that you are working hard."

Aside from pointing out your loved one's strengths, you must also reassure them that you will be there for them, no matter what.

Have Fun with Your Loved One

People with BPD experience intense negative emotions every single day of their life. That's tiring. So, to help a loved one with BPD, you must infuse positive emotions and experiences in your relationship. This means that you have to do fun activities.

As an example, here's a list of pleasurable activities that you could do with your loved one:

☐ Do group exercise like yoga or Zumba. These exercises create a cocktail of positive emotions and can increase one's self-confidence and self-esteem.

☐ Go on a picnic in a park. Being close to nature is good for someone who has BPD.

☐ Join a scavenger hunt.

☐ Watch the sunset together and enjoy its beauty.

☐ If you're in a romantic relationship with a borderline person, set a date night at least once a week.

☐ Go on a road trip or visit the nearest beach.

☐ Do fun physical activities together like surfing, or rock climbing.

☐ Build a garden together.

☐ See a funny movie.

☐ Wash each other's car.

☐ Go to Disneyland and make your partner's inner child happy.

☐ Enroll in a gym and lift weights together.

☐ Take funny and silly pictures and post them on Facebook or Instagram.

☐ Watch the sunrise together.

☐ Cook together.

- ☐ Plan a vacation.

- ☐ Engage in team sports like volleyball or basketball.

- ☐ Go bowling together.

- ☐ Go to a concert.

- ☐ Bike around the city with your loved one.

- ☐ Take your pets for a walk.

- ☐ Watch a fireworks display.

- ☐ Build a sandcastle.

- ☐ Play board games.

Doing fun activities can distract a borderline person from all the drama. It helps alleviate their pain and live a happier and more fulfilling life.

Create Healthy Boundaries

As mentioned earlier in this book, being in a relationship with someone who has BPD can be very challenging. It can mess you up if you allow it. People with BPD need boundaries.

People with BPD can turn something you did into a bigger issue and this can cause endless drama. Setting boundaries helps you snap them out of their delusional thinking. It helps you get them out of their "black and white" thinking pattern.

Boundaries make borderline people feel better. It calms them down and helps them manage their negative thoughts and even their emotions. This is the reason why you should give them a little tough love. Here's how you can do that:

1. Be clear about what you will and will not accept. You have to set your spiritual, emotional, and physical

limits. Remember that it's not healthy to drive to your loved one's house in the middle of the night just because they're having a tantrum.

2. Be direct when communicating your limits. Keep your sentences short and clear.

3. You are not responsible for your loved one's emotions. But you are accountable for your own actions and emotions. You are responsible for your own choices and decisions.

4. Be assertive, but calm and respectful. When you're asserting your boundaries, you have to be respectful and logical. People with BPD can get angry when you're imposing your boundaries. When this happens, stay calm, but be firm.

When you're dealing with someone with BPD, it's important to be firm and assertive, but at the same time, you have to communicate in a supportive, respectful, and loving way. And lastly, you should take care of yourself. You can't take care of another person if you're not well or you're also emotionally unstable. Spend time doing things that excite you and most of all, seek professional help if you need to. Living with a borderline person is stressful and taxing, so make sure that you look after yourself as well.

Conclusion

Thanks again for taking the time to read this book!

You should now have a good understanding of Borderline Personality Disorder and have some strategies for improving and eventually overcoming it! Remember, this book should not be taken as medical advice, and is simply a guide to BPD and its treatment options as we currently know them. Always seek professional medical help.

If you enjoyed this book, please take the time to leave me a review on Amazon. I appreciate your honest feedback, and it really helps me to continue producing high quality books.

Lightning Source UK Ltd.
Milton Keynes UK
UKHW020643131221
395574UK00008B/206